Time Pieces

for
Clarinet

Music through the Ages in 3 Volumes

Volume 2

**Selected and arranged by
Ian Denley**

**The Associated Board of
the Royal Schools of Music**

CONTENTS

Time Pieces for Clarinet

Volume 2

for Kate, Geoffrey and Michael

1637 **Balletto**
from the Second Book of Toccatas

Girolamo Frescobaldi
(1583–1643)

AB 2675

c.1720 Rondeau

Johann Krieger
(1651–1735)

Allegretto (♩ = c.108)

Clarinet in B♭

Piano

Krieger: *Rondeau* from *Intermediate Piano Book*, Volume 1. Edition Peters No. 4451.

AB 2675

1779 Menuetto e Trio

K. 315g No. 4

Wolfgang Amadeus Mozart
(1756–1791)

MENUETTO

Allegretto (♩ = c.108–116)

Menuetto D.C. al Fine

1795 **German Dance No. 6**

WoO8

Ludwig van Beethoven
(1770–1827)

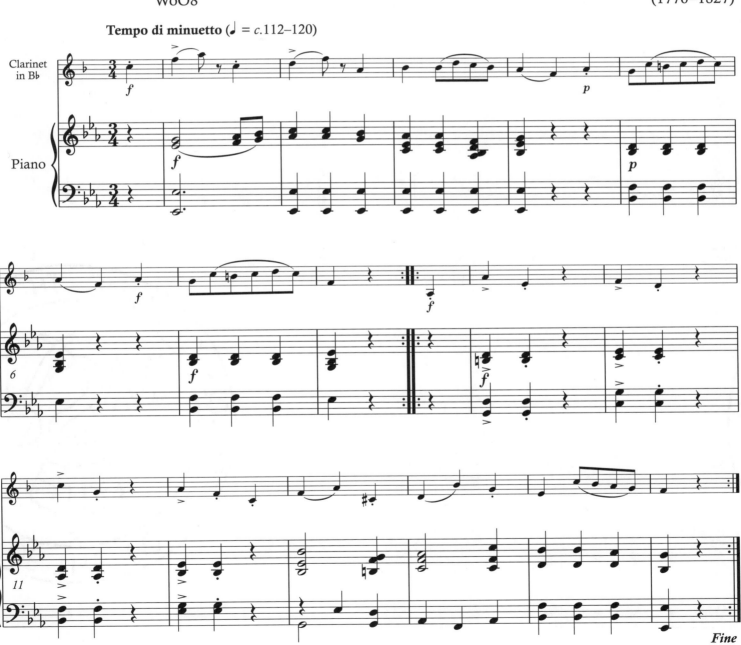

[TRIO]

D.C. al Fine

c.1810 Charlie is my darling

Traditional Scottish Air

1848 * * *

from *Album for the Young*, Op. 68

Robert Schumann
(1810–1856)

Langsam und mit Ausdruck zu spielen* (♩ = *c*.84–88)

*Langsam und mit Ausdruck zu spielen – Play slowly and with expression

langsamer – more slowly   *im Tempo* – in time   *etwas langsamer* – somewhat slower

This is one of four pieces in *Album for the Young* dedicated to the memory of Mendelssohn.
This piece, like two others in the album, has the enigmatic title of three black asterisks.

AB 2675

etwas langsamer*

im Tempo

1880 Nuit d'Étoiles
(Night of Stars)

Claude Debussy
(1862–1918)

morendo jusqu'à la fin – dying away to the end

1883 Lament

Henri Duparc
(1848–1933)

AB 2675

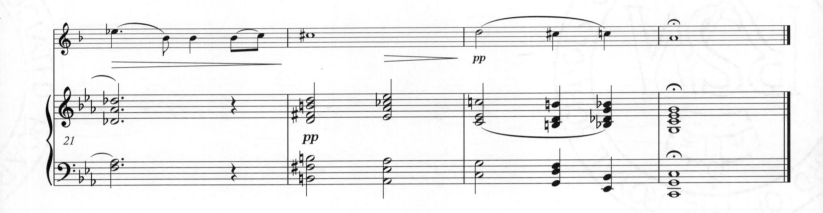

1889 **When a merry maiden marries**

from *The Gondoliers*

Arthur Sullivan
(1842–1900)

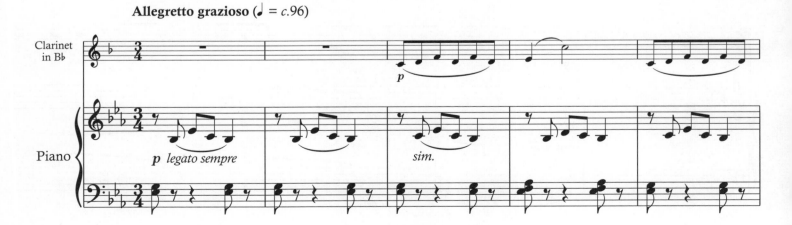

1902 Ballad

from *Merrie England*

Edward German
(1862–1936)

Allegretto semplice (♩ = *c*.96–100)

1916 **Lullaby**
Op. 2 No. 1

Oskar Merikanto
(1868–1924)

1926 A Little Song

from *Pictures of Childhood*

Aram Khachaturian
(1903–1978)

Andantino (♩ = *c*.88)

Clarinet
in B♭

Piano

1946 Dance

from *30 Pieces for Children*, Op. 27 No. 21

Dmitri Kabalevsky
(1904–1987)

Moderato scherzando ($\quad = c.126-132$)

1949 The Silent Lake

William Walton
(1902–1983)

from *Music for Children*, Book 1

AB 2675

1963 Siciliana

from *Ten easy pieces for piano*

Alexandre Tansman
(1897–1986)

1968 Close every door to me

from *Joseph and the Amazing Technicolor® Dreamcoat*

Music: Andrew Lloyd Webber
(b. 1948)
Lyrics: Tim Rice
(b. 1944)

Expressively (♩ = 96)

1992 Quand les rochers parlent . . .

Jean Hody
(b. 1935)

(When the rocks speak . . .)

from *Les reflets de la mer*

1996 Beginners Please!

No. 3 from *Six Duos*

Anthony Hedges
(b. 1931)

Reproduced by permission of Westfield Music, 76 Walkergate, Beverley HU17 9ER.

Music origination by
Barnes Music Engraving Ltd, East Sussex
Printed in England by Caligraving Ltd, Thetford, Norfolk

3:06